The Bone Giant

a North American tale
told by Evelyn Foster

Illustrated by Graham Philpot

W

FRANKLIN WATTS

First published in 2009 by
Franklin Watts
338 Euston Road
London
NW1 3BH

Franklin Watts Australia
Level 17/207 Kent Street
Sydney
NSW 2000

A CIP catalogue record for this book is available
from the British Library.

ISBN 978 0 7496 8598 0 (hbk)
ISBN 978 0 7496 8604 8 (pbk)

Series Editor: Jackie Hamley
Series Advisor: Dr Barrie Wade
Series Designer: Peter Scoulding

Printed in China

Franklin Watts is a division of
Hachette Children's Books,
an Hachette UK company
www.hachette.co.uk

This tale comes from
North America. Can you
find this area on a map?

Long ago, a brave called Eagle was playing by a lake when he met a stranger.

"Would you like to visit that island?" asked the stranger. "There are many beautiful birds there."

"Yes please!" Eagle replied. He loved animals and birds.

They sailed to the island
in the stranger's canoe,
pulled by three great
swans.

Eagle played with the birds and didn't notice the stranger slip away.

When night fell, he was
all alone.

Suddenly, Eagle heard
a voice. It sounded like
dry, old bones.

"Boy, boy!" creaked
the voice.

Eagle looked and gasped.
In the grass sat a skeleton!

13

"The stranger who brought you here is really a bone giant," said the skeleton.

"Beware! He will come tonight to kill you. You must hide in that tree."

"Thank you!" said Eagle.
He picked up a large
stone and hid in the tree.

17

Later on, the stranger came back. Now he was a huge giant made of bones.

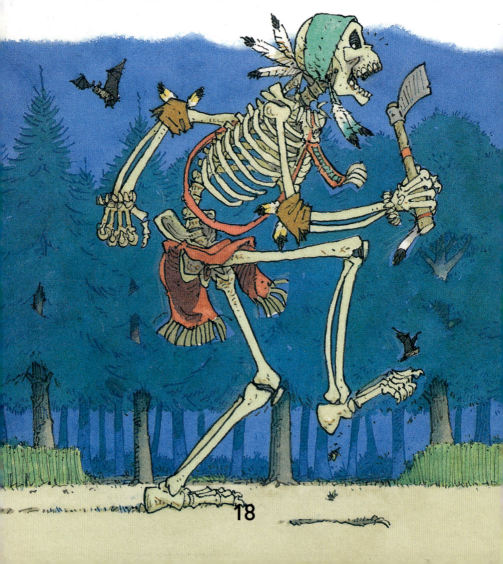

He sniffed the air and
turned to the tree where
Eagle was hiding.

Eagle flung the stone …

… and the giant crumbled!

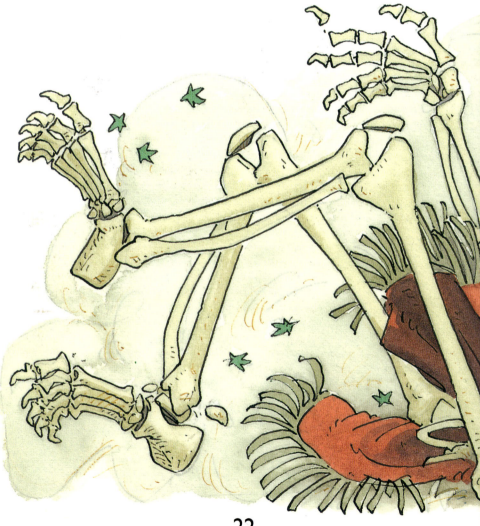

Eagle crept out and found
a boy sitting where the
skeleton had been.

"Thank you. By killing the giant, you have brought me back to life!" the boy said.

The two boys sailed
home in the canoe.

Eagle and the boy became friends. They often played by the lake, but they never talked to strangers again.

Puzzle 1

Put these pictures in the correct order.
Now tell the story in your own words.
What different endings can you think of?

Puzzle 2

brave   foolish

scared

honest   nasty

gentle

helpful   mean

kind

Choose the correct adjectives for each character. Which adjectives are incorrect? Turn over to find the answers.

Answers

Puzzle 1

The correct order is: 1f, 2c, 3b, 4d, 5e, 6a

Puzzle 2

Eagle: the correct adjectives are brave, foolish
The incorrect adjective is scared

The bone giant: the correct adjective is nasty
The incorrect adjectives are gentle, honest

The skeleton: the correct adjectives are helpful, kind
The incorrect adjective is mean